Book 3

Robert Pace

Music for Piano

Illustrated by Ray Koos

Parade

Keep a steady tempo and observe the dynamics as you play this march.

I. Fanfare - oct. disp.
II. mel. var.
III. double the rhythm of marchbass.

Blow the Man Down

Play the right hand softly and bring out the melody in the left hand.

Sea Chantey

4

Cradle Song

Notice that the right and left hands move almost entirely in parallel motion.

TÜRK

Marching Song

Find the measures that are alike.

TÜRK

Au Clair De La Lune

What is the form of this song?

French Folk Song

Old Christmas Carol

Find the measures with this rhythm:

Now find the measures with this rhythm:

French Carol

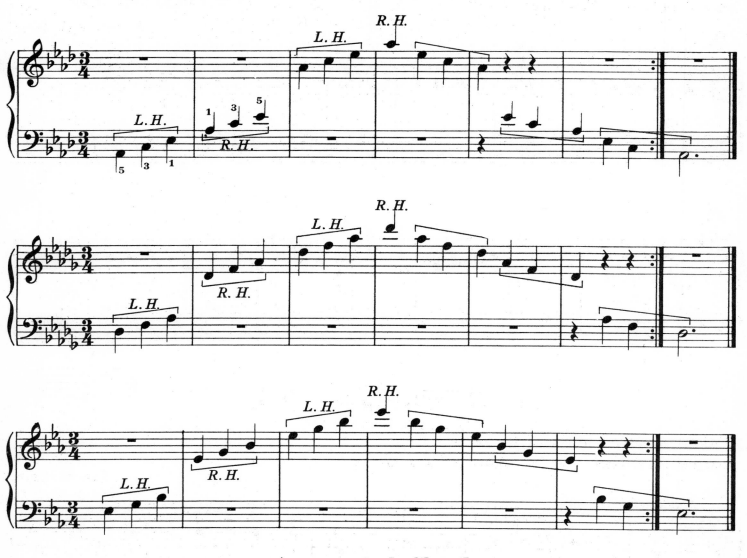

Major Arpeggios

First, practice each arpeggio slowly. Do not let it become uneven as you develop speed.

Augmented Chords

An *augmented* chord is made by raising the top note of a major chord. Notice the sign for double sharp (✕) in the F♯ augmented chord. Fill in the correct chords in the bass clef.

D maj.　　D aug.　　E♭ maj.　　E♭ aug.　　F maj.　　F aug.　　F♯ maj.　　F♯ aug.

Sweet Betsy from Pike

Roll the bass chords softly from the bottom note to the top.

American Folk Song

Sailing

Find the lines that are exactly alike. How are the 2nd and 4th lines similar?

GODFREY MARKS

With a gentle swing

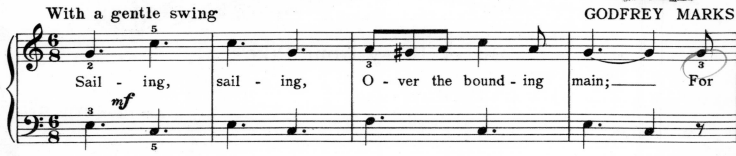

Sail - ing, sail - ing, O - ver the bound - ing main;_____ For

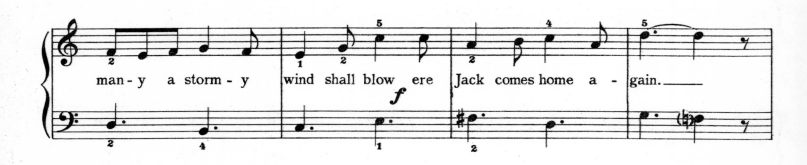

man - y a storm - y wind shall blow ere Jack comes home a - gain._____

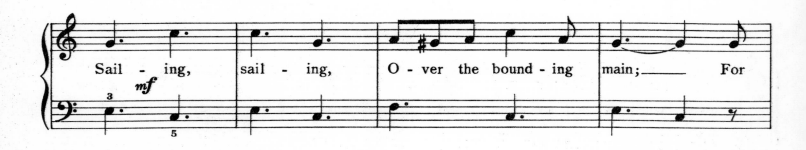

Sail - ing, sail - ing, O - ver the bound - ing main;_____ For

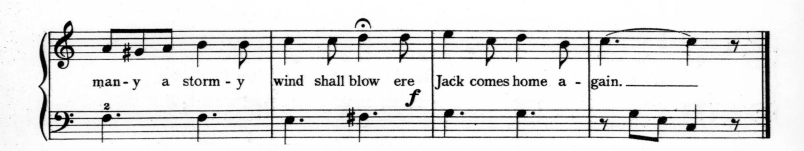

man - y a storm - y wind shall blow ere Jack comes home a - gain._____

Going Places

Play this piece with firm hands and nicely curved fingers. Make sure that each note is sounded.

I in G minor
II open Fifths
III

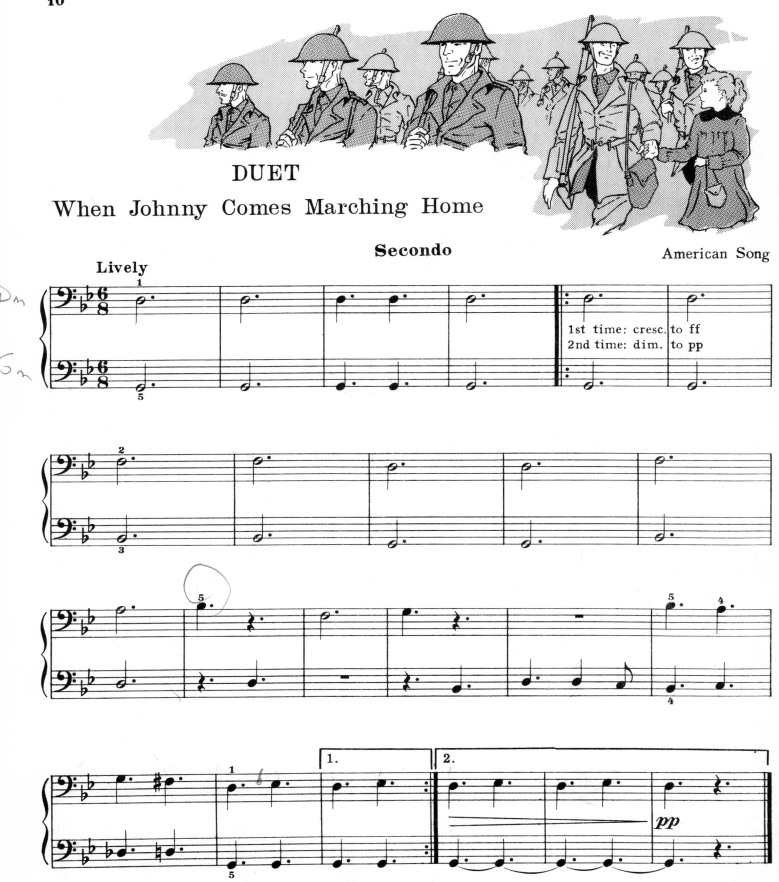

DUET
When Johnny Comes Marching Home

Secondo

American Song

Primo

Serenade

This folk melody uses an ascending scale, while "Morris Dance," below, is based on a descending scale.

Bohemian Folk Melody

Morris Dance

English Folk Melody

Using the same fingering, transpose each of these pieces to the key of D major.

C Major Scale

Find the groupings of three and four notes in this C major scale. All sharp keys (except F♯ major and the left hand of B major) follow this same pattern of fingering.

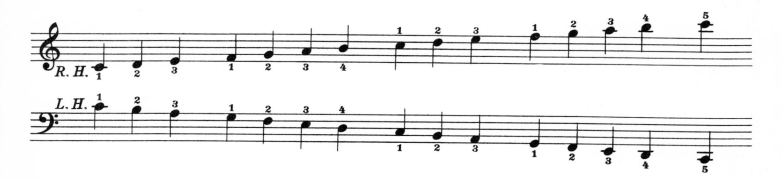

Before playing the scale as written below, play each hand alone, following these simple rules:

1. Keep your fingers curved and play on the finger-tips.
2. Avoid a break or "bump" as you pass your thumb under or your third finger across.
3. Don't rush or slow up. Keep a steady tempo.
4. Make each tone match the others. No accents on the thumbs!
5. Remember that your 3rd fingers always play together.

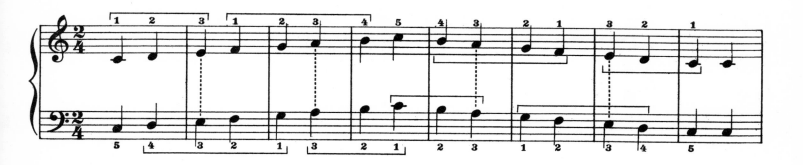

Minuet

Find all of the sequences in this melody.

This is a *three-part* form (A B A)

Winter Is Gone

Look for all repeated melody patterns.

Folk Song

Chorale

Johann Sebastian Bach, whose family had been town-musicians for generations, was born in Eisenach in 1685. Bach first learned violin from his father, and later his older brother, Johann Christoph, taught him to play keyboard instruments. He became a fine organist and wrote some of the world's greatest church music. His wife, Anna Magdalena, was also a musician and frequently helped him with his work. This "Chorale" is taken from the *Anna Magdalena Bach Book* which contains many pieces written especially for the Bach children.

Major Arpeggios

G Major Scale

DUET
Roll That Brown Jug

Folk Song

Secondo

Primo

HARMONIZING MELODIES

Flemish Folk Song

Fill in a waltz bass for this melody. Use the I, IV, and V₇ chords.

French Folk Song

First write the number of the correct chord under each measure, then fill in the chords.

America, the Beautiful

S. A. WARD

Menuette

This "Menuette" was written for Mozart's sister, Nannerl.

SIGHTREADING AND TRANSPOSING

Here are three melodies to sightread, each in a different meter. Play each one slowly, several times, then transpose up and down one-half step.

1.

2.

3.

Pancho

The syncopated rhythm in this folk tune is typically Spanish. Before you play the song, practice these rhythms.

tap your right hand

tap your left hand

Keep the left hand going and change your right hand to the syncopation.

tap your right hand

tap your left hand

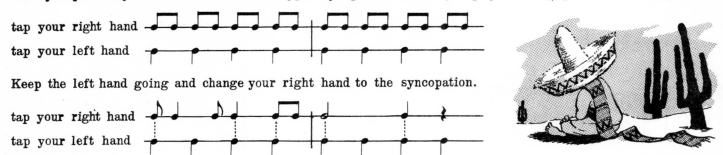

Brazilian Folk Tune

Moderato

ACHIEVEMENT TEST

1. Write the correct chords for this melody.

2. Mark the repetitions (R) and sequences (S) in this melody. Sightread, then transpose to G and E♭ major.

3. Write your best answer to this question, then fill in the chords.

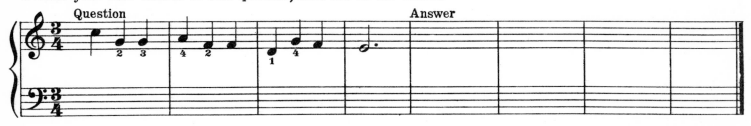

4. Identify the following chords:

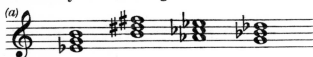

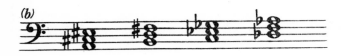

		Possible Score	My Score
Part 1		25	
Part 2		25	
Part 3		30	
Part 4a		10	
Part 4b		10	
	Total	100	

Long, Long Ago

THOMAS H. BAYLY

Ancient Hymn

Gregorian Hymn

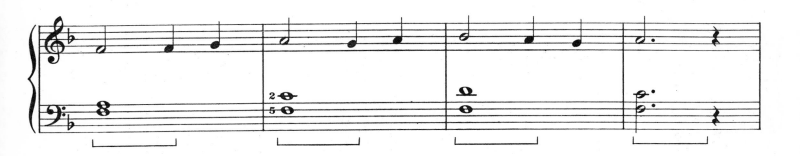

Solemn Sam

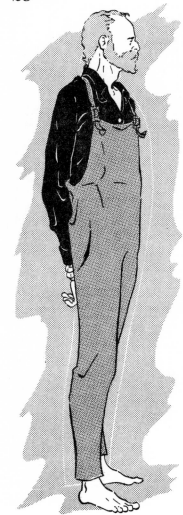

Dolefully

Slumber Song

Norwegian Folk Song

Slowly

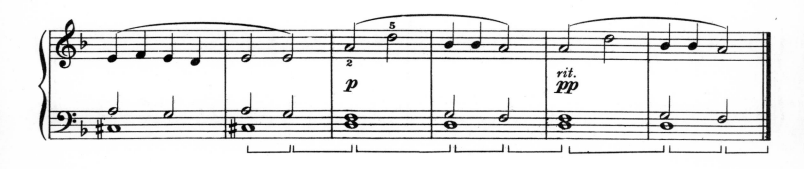

Peasant Dance

The vigorous rhythm in this folk song makes it particularly suitable for a ring dance. Practice these rhythms, then play the song.

Now keep the same beat, but tap the exact rhythm of the song.

Folk Song

DUET
She'll Be Comin' 'Round the Mountain

Secondo

American Folk Song

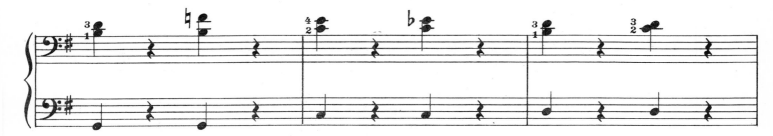

Primo

Carefree

Play a "block chord" accompaniment the first time you play the melody:  Notice that the melody consists of chord tones. Then play the piece as written.

German Folk Song

SD III, pp. 15, 16, 33

Solitude

Contra Dance

BEETHOVEN

Trolls and Leprechauns

Always look through any music before sightreading it. In this piece, find the repeated patterns in the right hand. What makes the rhythm easy to play?

Jim Along Josie

Play as written, then transpose to E♭ and F major.

Hey, Jim a-long,   Jim a-long, Jo - sie,   Hey, Jim a-long,   Jim a-long, Joe.

Hey, Jim a-long,   Jim a-long, Jo - sie,   Hey, Jim a-long,   Jim a-long, Joe.

Fine

Face to the cen-ter,   Hands on your knees!   Clap three times and   turn a-round please.

DC al Fine

SD III, p. 35

Shoo Fly

Not all of the tones of the I and V₇ chords are used in this accompaniment.
Write the number under each chord.

American Song

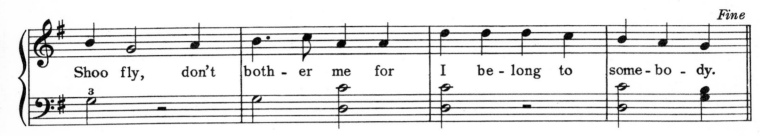

Harmonize this melody, then write the bass part you have created.

Twilight

Here are two songs with three-measure phrases. Play them smoothly and watch for the tied notes.

Slavonic Folk Song

Day Dreams

Little Piece

SCHUMANN

Toy Trumpet

Some Other Mice

The right hand in this song is written in the whole tone scale (all tones are one whole step apart) and the left hand is composed of three notes: F♯, G♯, and A♯. You could also harmonize the melody with augmented chords in the left hand.

Adapted

Dolefully

DUET
Turkey In the Straw

Secondo

Square Dance Tune

DUET

Turkey In the Straw

Square Dance Tune

Primo

Caissons

¢ means two beats per measure and the half notes get one beat. ¢

Count 1 & 2 & 1 & 2 &

EDMUND GRUBER

Marching tempo

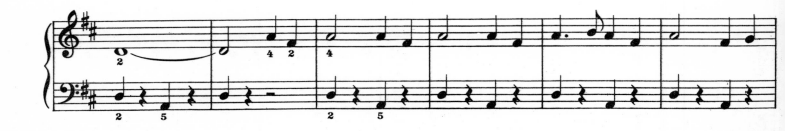

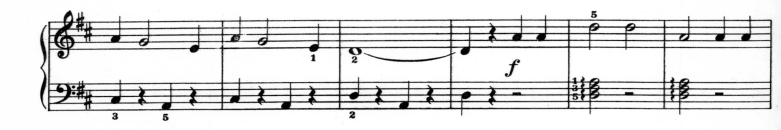

Home On The Range

Cowboy Song

Tarantella

Minuet

HAYDN

ACHIEVEMENT TEST

1. Finish and harmonize this melody.

2. Sightread and transpose to D minor.

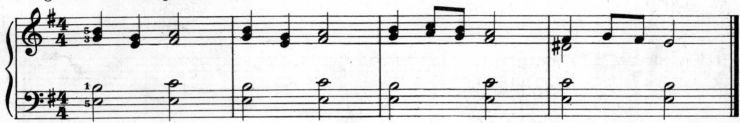

3. Write and play a D major scale.

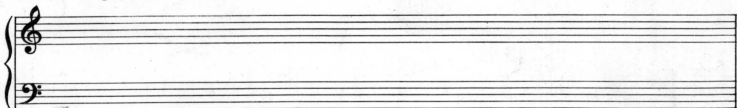

4. Write the following chords:

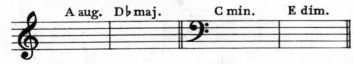

5. Complete the following intervals:

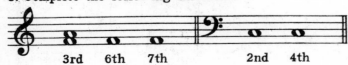

	Possible Score	My Score
Part 1	20	
Part 2	20	
Part 3	20	
Part 4	20	
Part 5	20	
Total	100	